DEMOCRACY NOW!

MANDARIN

intro

SINCE the recent transformation of Mega-City One into a 'Necropolis' by the Dark Judges, questions have been raised as to the competence of our own Judges. Are they fit to rule? Can they be trusted? Is it time for a change? As the call for 'Democracy Now!' sounds ever louder around the city, MEGARAMA explores the background to the fall and rise of the democrats and unveils the astonishing lengths to which the Judges have gone in an effort to cling onto power...

MEGARAMA *Democracy Then?*

After holding sway in the old United States of America for almost three centuries, democracy formally came to an end in the Mega-Cities of the no longer quite so 'United States' in 2071. Under the overall leadership, albeit temporarily, of the legendary Judge Solomon, Mega-Cities One, Two and Three (the latter soon to become Texas City) adopted a new form of government...the rule of the Judges. The people, appalled by the legacy of 'democracy' – a country ravaged with the grisly results of nuclear war – embraced this new order with open arms.

But how has their trust been repaid? Have the Judges been worthy of the historic burden placed upon them? A review of major events since 2071 makes uncomfortable reading for the Judges: a destructive civil war with Texas City; a robot rebellion that laid waste to large areas of Mega-City One; the shameful and tyrannical reign of the mad Chief Judge Cal; a new atomic war with the Sov-Block, wiping out half the city, and, most recently, more than 60 million citizens killed by the Dark Judges. This is the grim reality of life under the Judges. Little wonder, then, that the democratic underground movement has grown ever stronger during the Judges' 40 year rule.

The Judges claim that the problems they have had to face can hardly be blamed on them. They say that similar 'difficulties' have beset Mega-Cities all over the world and that the democrats would only make things worse. Yet they have agreed to stake everything on a referendum they seem certain to lose. Just under a year ago, in late November 2112, literally in the wake of the 'Necropolis' debacle, a Senior Judge Review proposed a vote in Mega-City One that may well see the return of democracy after four decades. Judge Dredd himself is a strong proponent of the referendum, firmly believing that the Judges need a new mandate if they are to retain power in the shadow of the 'Necropolis'.

Just five years ago, the prospect of a return to democracy was unimaginable. The democratic movement was a disorganised collection of splinter groups whose message went almost entirely unheard. On 13th March 2108, however, one act by a small number of activists belonging to a group called 'The Democratic Tendency' changed the whole face of the struggle for democracy overnight.

In a deliberate and calculated action, Hester Hyman, Franklin Lund, J. William Williams and Roofer Tuttle stormed the studios of Channel 48's popular breakfast show. They were armed and ready to fight, but in fact hurt no-one as they broadcast the main demands of their new 'Democratic Charter'. They called for: 1) 'An immediate return to democratic principles. The people must control the Judges! The Judges should not control the people!'; 2) 'The return of basic freedoms taken away over decades of oppression!'; and 3) 'A repeal of the harsh penalties for minor infringements!'

Perhaps this message alone would have been enough to kick-start the cause of 'democracy', but this must be considered unlikely. After all, its impact on an audience more interested in the life and loves of vid-star, Romeo Hepp, or even the musings of Bishop Desmond Snodgrass, was probably minimal. No, it was the sacrifice made by the four members of the 'Democratic Tendency' in choosing death before surrender that provided the inspiration to the democratic movement which was to prove so important in the months and years to come.

When they blasted their way into the studio to recapture Channel 48 from the terrorists, the Judges had no way of knowing how much trouble they were bringing down upon their own heads. By killing Hester Hyman and her cohorts, they gave the democratic movement what it sorely needed... four martyrs around whom to unite. Hester Hyman herself turned out to be as powerful a symbol for the democrats as Judge Dredd is for the Mega-City One Judges.

Hester Hyman was just an ordinary citizen who wanted a decent future for her children. She could see them growing up into frightened people, only good for taking orders from the Judges. Hester saw her children's future and it terrified her so much that she was willing to sacrifice her life to change it. It was her very 'ordinariness' that made Hester Hyman such a potent symbol. She proved that anyone could stand up to the Judges and her death symbolised everything that was wrong with their system.

In her honour, leading democrats formed the Hester Hyman Trust, an umbrella organisation incorporating all the major democratic splinter groups - 'The Sons of the Constitution', 'The Freedom League', 'The Democratic Urge' and 'The Committee for the Restoration of Civil Liberties.' In the course of little more than a year, these previously ineffectual splinters built up a remarkable following. By July 2109 they were actually strong enough to organise a mass demonstration against the Judges.

While the democrats remained weak, the Judges were prepared to tolerate them with the confident air of an Otto Sump lookalike entering an 'ugly' competition. However, when Blondel Dupre, leader of 'The Democratic Urge', announced the formation of 'The Democratic Charter Group' and the plan to march on the Grand Hall of Justice, the Judges had to take notice. Based around the charter of 'The Democratic Tendency', this new group was an adjunct to the Hester Hyman Trust and it was to act as a rallying organisation for the millions of pro-democracy citizens who, it was hoped, would join the march.

MEGARAMA has managed to uncover evidence that proves the Judges set about sabotaging this march from the start, so concerned about the political ramifications of it was the then Chief Judge Silver. It is a well-established fact that hundreds, and possibly thousands, of agent provocateurs were placed on the march and it was they who started all the trouble, provoking the violence which the organisers were so desperate to avoid. However, what is less well known is the way in which the Judges whittled down the democrat leaders, just before the march actually took place.

Bethann Rosie, leader of 'The Committee for the Restoration of Civil Liberties', was accused of bigamy by the Judges and branded by the press as someone of very low moral values. In fact, her only 'crime' was to sign her name 'Beth Ann' by mistake on her second divorce papers. The Judges claimed this made the divorce invalid and as a result she was guilty of bigamy. The legal wrangling lasted just three months before the Judges dropped the charges, due to the weakness of their case, but the damage was already done and Bethann Rosie was unable to take part in the march.

Though no charges were brought against Morton Phillips, leader of 'The Freedom League', it seems that undercover Judge 'Wally Squad' agents were able to discredit him by accusing him of being a Sov-collaborator during the 'Apocalypse War'. These insinuations had no basis in fact, but Morton too was forced to withdraw from the march.

Gort Hyman, Hester's widower, came to share her vision of a society not ruled by Judges, and spoke out strongly in favour of the march at first. But then he seemed to change his mind completely and condemned it as a 'march of insanity', MEGARAMA has managed to unearth the truth behind this incredible about-face. Unable to find any blemish in Gort's past to blackmail him with, the Judges simply threatened to induct his two children into the Academy of Law. Reluctantly, Gort was forced to go along with the Judges and denounce the march in public. It seemed that Kenzal Davitchek, leader of 'The Sons of the Constitution', had no stomach for the democratic march in the end and that he gave up half way. In truth, the Judges picked him up the night before for having a vid-slug two days overdue and kept him on his feet all night with no food or

water. When he was released on the morning of the march he was in no fit state to complete it.

Blondel Dupre was the only democrat leader the Judges allowed to complete the march, so she was well placed to be a scapegoat for any trouble caused. When violence broke out on the march, Blondel, despite trying to calm things down, was caught right in the thick of it. She was arrested along with thousands of others, charged with a breach of the peace and assault, and sent to the cubes.

From the evidence we have compiled for MEGARAMA there can be no doubt that the Judges deliberately undermined the democratic march of 2109. It seems that the late Chief Judge Silver was willing to authorise any action designed to crush the march, but his attempt to set back the cause of democracy may well have backfired in the long run.

It is widely believed that Judge Dredd, who was instrumental in carrying out Silver's orders, now feels that his treatment of the marchers was wrong. Shortly before the Dark Judges came to Mega-City One, rumours were rife that Dredd was considering retirement over that very issue. Instead, he merely freed all 63 prisoners still doing time in the cubes who had been arrested on the march. Among them was a very surprised Blondel Dupre. Later, when the Dark Judges had been defeated, it was very much at Judge Dredd's insistence that the referendum on who should run the city was called.

Dredd has gone on record to say that he believes the Judges will win the vote, but most of the pundits and opinion-pollsters would dis-agree. It would seem then that the over-zealous actions of former Chief Judge Silver in trying to stamp out the democratic movement, has opened the door wider for democracy than at any time in the last 40 years. Only time, and the will of the people, will tell whether that door swings fully open, or slams back in the democrats' faces.

MEGARAMA REPORTER - Mike Butcher

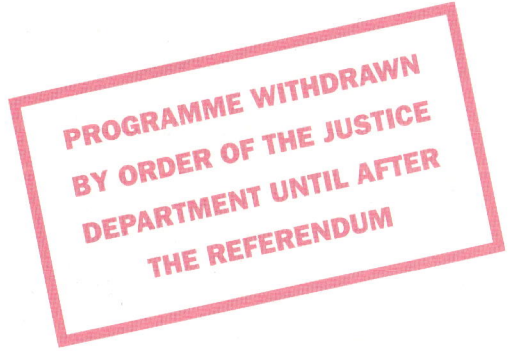

PROGRAMME WITHDRAWN BY ORDER OF THE JUSTICE DEPARTMENT UNTIL AFTER THE REFERENDUM

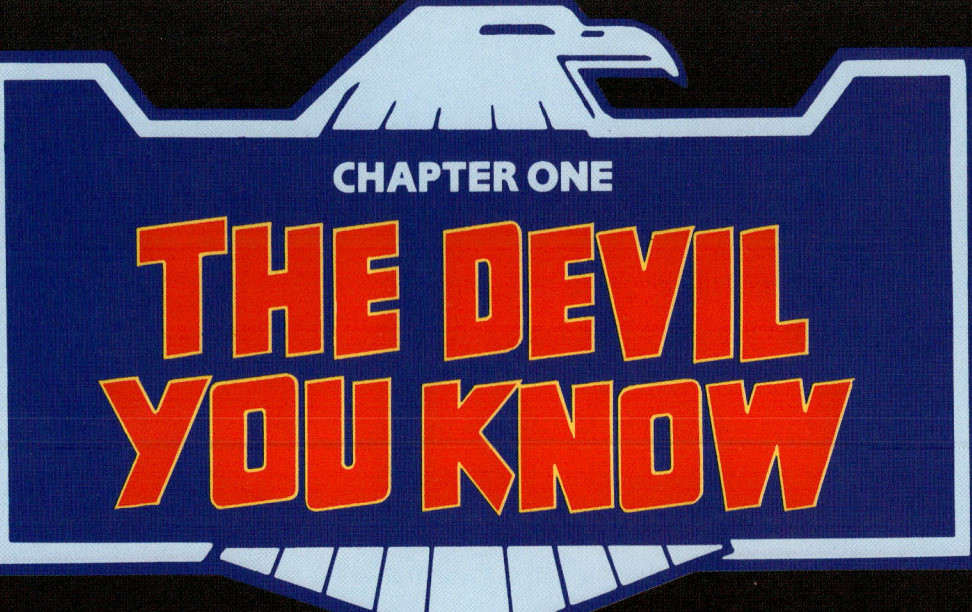

CHAPTER ONE
THE DEVIL YOU KNOW

Brrrinngg brrrinnngg!

Bleep!

HI THERE! YOU'RE THROUGH TO **FREECALL REFERENDUM HOTLINE!**

THE **REFERENDUM** IS NOW ONLY THREE WEEKS AWAY.

IF YOU ARE A **LEGAL CITIZEN** OVER **SIXTEEN** YEARS OF AGE AND CURRENTLY NEITHER A SERVING PRISONER NOR AN INMATE OF ANY PSYCHIATRIC INSTITUTION, **YOU** WILL BE ELIGIBLE TO PARTICIPATE.

YEAH, BUT, UH... WHAT'S IT ALL MEAN?

THE **ISSUE** AT STAKE IS THIS: DO WE CONTINUE UNDER THE **PRESENT** SYSTEM WHEREBY THE CITIZENS' ELECTED REPRESENTATIVE BODY IS EMPOWERED TO MAKE REPRESENTATIONS, BUT WHERE ULTIMATE LEGISLATIVE POWER RESIDES WITH THE **JUDGES** – ?

OR DO WE RETURN TO THE **FORMER** SYSTEM WHEREBY THE JUDGES – OR SOME **ALTERNATIVE** AGENCY – RETURN TO A STRICT LAW ENFORCEMENT ROLE IN ACCORDANCE WITH STATUTES ENACTED BY THE CITIZENS' ELECTED REPRESENTATIVE BODY, IN WHOM ULTIMATE LEGISLATIVE POWER RESIDES?

JUDICIAL CONTROL – OR DEMOCRACY.

HUH?

OH.

NOW, IF YOU LOOK ON YOUR REMOTE YOU'LL SEE A BUTTON MARKED "INTERFACE-CH MAINFRAME". GOT IT?

UH... YEAH.

THAT BUTTON WILL PUT YOU IN DIRECT TOUCH WITH **BARNEY,** THE CITY HALL COMPUTER...

DEMOLITION DROIDS! GOING TO TAKE MORE THAN A BULLET TO STOP THEM —!

DREDD'S RUNNING!

CHICKEN!

CLEAR THE WAY!

KEEP COMING!

FOLLOW ME!

CLOSE!

GET **BACK**! THERE'S GOING TO BE TROUBLE!

KKRUNK!

ONE—TWO—THREE—FOUR! NO MORE JUDGES ANYMORE!

FIVE—SIX—SEVEN—EIGHT! THE PEOPLE GONNA LEGISLATE!

JUDGES ARE LEAVING THE PRE-REFERENDUM MEETING NOW.—

JUDGE DREDD! IT'S A VIRTUAL CERTAINTY THAT ON OCTOBER 1ST THE RULE OF THE JUDGES WILL AT LAST COME TO AN END—

I DON'T AGREE.

YOU THINK THE VOTE MIGHT GO **YOUR** WAY? BUT WHAT CAN YOU OFFER EXCEPT... MORE OF THE SAME?

EXACTLY. PEOPLE KNOW WHERE THEY STAND WITH US. I THINK THEY APPRECIATE THAT.

WE'RE NOT PERFECT. THERE MAY BE ROOM FOR US TO TAKE MORE ACCOUNT OF THE CITIZENS' WISHES — SOME LAWS MAY BE IN NEED OF REVISION — BUT OTHERWISE, NOTHING'S CHANGED.

DISCIPLINE, GOOD ORDER, THE RIGID APPLICATION OF THE LAW — THOSE ARE THE PRINCIPLES ON WHICH WE STAND.

AND YOU THINK PEOPLE WILL VOTE FOR **THAT**?

I DO. BETTER THE DEVIL YOU KNOW?

WHAT'S THE ALTERNATIVE? A RETURN TO THE **JURY** SYSTEM?

WHY NOT?

AND WHILE WE'RE TIED UP IN **RED TAPE**, WHO'S WATCHING THE STREETS.?

WHEN SOME CREEP'S HOLDING A KNIFE TO YOUR THROAT, WHO DO YOU WANT TO SEE RIDING UP... **ME** — OR YOUR **ELECTED REPRESENTATIVE**?

THINK ABOUT IT.

JUDGE **GRICE**! RUMOUR IS THE DECISION TO HOLD A REFERENDUM WAS NOT UNANIMOUS — THAT THERE IS, IN FACT, A LARGE NUCLEUS OF JUDGES WHO ARE STILL VIOLENTLY **OPPOSED** TO THE PROSPECT...?

NO COMMENT.

22.30 HOURS.

THE ROBOTS FAILED.

I HEARD.

DAMN HIM! HE'S ALWAYS BEEN A LUCKY JUDGE!

IT'S A BAD SIGN. I **KNEW** WE SHOULDN'T HAVE STARTED THIS!

WE'VE BEEN THROUGH IT ALL BEFORE. WE **HAVE** TO DO IT.

WELL **I** DON'T LIKE IT!

I NEVER LIKED IT, TURNING ON ONE OF OUR OWN! IT'S A CRIME, FOR GRUD'S SAKE — WE'RE COMMITTING MURDER!

MURDER ? WHAT KIND OF FOOL'S TALK IS THAT ? IF THE REFERENDUM GOES AHEAD IT'S THE **END** OF US — YOU KNOW THAT, CROSBY.

GRUD! DID YOU HEAR HIM TONIGHT ?

"OH, YES, THE CITIZENS WILL VOTE FOR US. WE'RE GOING TO KEEP ON KNOCKING SEVEN KINDS OF HELL OUT OF THEM BUT THEY'LL STILL VOTE FOR US, BECAUSE THAT'S THE WAY THEY **LIKE** IT!"

HAHAHAHA-HAHAAAAA-HAHAHAHA!

THE MAN'S MAD! HE'LL PLUNGE THIS CITY INTO CHAOS — ANARCHY!

FOR THE GOOD OF EVERYONE HE HAS TO BE **REMOVED**. THEN WE CAN STOP THIS REFERENDUM NONSENSE BEFORE IT GETS OUT OF HAND.

SWAZE — YOU SAID SOMEONE IN CENTRAL CONTROL IS WITH US ? I WANT YOU TO GET ON TO HIM.

HER.

HER. WE WON'T LEAVE IT TO ROBOTS **THIS** TIME.

DISCIPLINE, GOOD ORDER, THE RIGID APPLICATION OF THE LAW — THOSE ARE THE PRINCIPLES ON WHICH WE STAND.

AND YOU THINK PEOPLE WILL VOTE FOR **THAT**?

I DO.

BETTER THE DEVIL YOU KNOW?

WHAT'S THE ALTERNATIVE? A RETURN TO THE **JURY** SYSTEM?

AND WHILE WE'RE TIED UP IN **RED TAPE**, WHO'S WATCHING THE STREETS?

WHEN SOME CREEP'S HOLDING A KNIFE TO YOUR THROAT, WHO DO YOU WANT TO SEE RIDING UP... **ME** — OR YOUR **ELECTED REPRESENTATIVE**?

THINK ABOUT IT.

BLONDEL DUPRE, LEADER OF THE DEMOCRATIC COALITION — BETTER THE DEVIL YOU KNOW?

HE'S USING SCARE TACTICS TO FRIGHTEN PEOPLE INTO VOTING FOR HIM. HE MAKES IT SOUND AS IF THERE'LL BE NO FORM OF LAW ENFORCEMENT UNDER DEMOCRACY — AS IF CRIMINALS WOULD BE RUNNING WILD ON THE STREETS.

IT'S SO OBVIOUS IT'S LAUGHABLE!

WOULD YOU SEE THE JUDGES BEING RETAINED?

MY OWN PARTY, NO. WE FAVOUR A RETURN TO A SEPARATE POLICE FORCE AND JUDICIARY. BUT THAT, OF COURSE, WOULD DEPEND ON THE VOTERS. THE REAL CONTEST WON'T BEGIN UNTIL **AFTER** THE REFERENDUM.

IGNATZ BERNSTEIN OF THE ELECTORAL STUDY GROUP — DO THE JUDGES HAVE A CHANCE?

DREDD IS PROBABLY THE ONLY MAN IN THE CITY WHO THINKS SO!

WE CAN DISMISS THAT AS AN IRRELEVANCE AND GET DOWN TO THE REAL MATTER AT ISSUE — WHAT FORM OF GOVERNMENT WE WILL HAVE WHEN THE ELECTORAL PROCESS IS OVER.

FOR INSTANCE, DO WE GO FOR SOME FORM OF PROPORTIONAL REPRESENTATION OR A SIMPLE FIRST PAST THE POST SYSTEM? DO WE ADOPT A PRESIDENTIAL OR A PARLIAMENTARY STYLE OF GOVERNMENT? WE MIGHT AS WELL START DISCUSSING THESE ISSUES NOW.

AUGUST WINDY OF THE SKEPTICS — YOU WANT TO COME IN THERE.

UH, YEAH.

I'D JUST LIKE TO ASK — ASSUMING WE DO ACTUALLY HAVE A REFERENDUM, WHICH I DOUBT — WHAT MAKES ANYONE THINK THE JUDGES ARE GOING TO **ACCEPT** THE RESULT?

WE HAVE JUDGE DREDD'S WORD. WHATEVER ELSE I MAY THINK OF HIM, I BELIEVE HE'LL BEHAVE HONOURABLY.

YOU'LL FORGIVE ME IF I REMAIN SCEPTICAL.

I'LL FORGIVE YOU, MY SON.

BISHOP DESMOND SNODGRASS — WHERE DOES THE CHURCH STAND?

OH, I THINK VERY MUCH WHERE IT ALWAYS HAS.

IT'S ON THE CORNER OF MILLET STREET, JUST ACROSS FROM THE DELI.

IT'S GOT A BIG STEEPLE AND STAINED GLASS WINDOWS AND STUFF. YOU CAN'T MISS IT.

CONTROL TO DREDD! CALLER REPORTS DISTURBANCE, AMOX STOREHOUSE ON KELSEY.

I'VE GOT TWO PRISONERS HERE, CONTROL. CAN YOU ASSIGN ANOTHER UNIT?

WHOEVER SICCED THOSE ROBOTS ON YOU GOT THE SERIAL NUMBERS, ALL RIGHT — BUT THEY MISSED SOMETHING ELSE. ONE OF THEM HAD A REPLACEMENT ROTOR JOINT — BRIT-CIT JOB, SPECIAL IMPORT.

I TRACED IT BACK TO A ROBOT OWNED BY SEARS CONSTRUCT, ONE OF TWO **STOLEN** FOUR MONTHS AGO.

BLOOD...

SO FIND THE THIEF...

THE CREEPS HAVE ALREADY **BEEN** FOUND — THEY'RE DOING **THREE** IN THE CUBES. THE ROBOTS WERE **RECOVERED.**

THIS IS THE INTERESTING BIT. SEARS CONSTRUCT WENT BUST. THE ROBOTS WERE **NEVER** COLLECTED.

STAIRS ARE OUT.

ELEVATOR COMING

FOR THE PAST THREE MONTHS THEY'VE BEEN STORED IN THE **JUSTICE DEPARTMENT POUND !**

THEY **WHAT** — ?

THAT DAMNED LUCK OF HIS!

MY GRUD, IT'LL ALL BE OUT NOW! WE'VE GOT TO —

YOUR LAWGIVER.

THAT'S IT, THEN...

AM I...UNDER ARREST?

OUR ORDERS ARE JUST TO DETAIN YOU HERE.

" JUDGE DREDD IS ON HIS WAY."

HOW MANY **MORE** DID YOU CORRUPT, GRICE?

HOW MANY JUDGES HAVE YOU SUCKED INTO YOUR SORDID LITTLE CONSPIRACY, EH?

YOU'D BE SURPRISED.

RECRUITS WEREN'T HARD TO FIND. YOU'RE DANGEROUS, DREDD. YOU HAVE TO BE REMOVED.

I'M DANGEROUS?

I'M DANGEROUS?

SMAAACKK!

WHAMMM!

THEN AGAIN, WE CAN'T BE **ABSOLUTELY** SURE A CRIME IS BEING COMMITTED...

NO...NO, TRUE...

THEY COULD, FOR INSTANCE, BE PLAYING A **BOISTEROUS** GAME OF SOME SORT...

KRUNK!

WHHUMP!

OR REDECORATING THE OFFICE. THAT MAKES A LOT OF NOISE.

YES, I'M SURE YOU'RE RIGHT. THAT MUST BE IT.

THOP!

WAKKKK!

SPOT OF REDECORATION.

CRAAAASSH!

NICE.

YOU PIECE OF GARBAGE, YOU KNOW WHAT YOU'VE DONE? YOU'VE **LOST** IT FOR US!

YOU'RE A FOOL, DREDD! YOU... YOU THINK WE EVER HAD A CHANCE? THE PEOPLE **HATE** US!

MAYBE THEY DO, GRICE. THEY SURE DON'T LOVE US. BUT FOR ALL THAT, I'LL TELL YOU WHAT ELSE THEY DO... THEY **TRUST** US.

FOR ALL OUR FAULTS, FOR ALL OUR MISTAKES, THE PEOPLE KNOW THAT WE STAND BY OUR PRINCIPLES AND **WE DON'T BEND**. THAT MEANS A LOT MORE THAN YOU MIGHT THINK.

AND NOW THEY'RE GOING TO HEAR ABOUT **YOU**, GRICE — YOU AND THE REST OF THEM.

AND WHAT ARE THEY GOING TO THINK THEN? BETTER THE DEVIL YOU KNOW...?

I DON'T THINK SO.

AND MAYBE THEY'LL BE RIGHT.

CHAPTER TWO
TWILIGHT'S LAST GLEAMING

MEGA-CITY ONE, NOVEMBER 2113...

REFERENDUM DAY.

DON'T MOVE, MAJOR. WE—

RELAX, DEKKER.

MAJOR!

MAJOR TOOK THE EASY WAY OUT.

MMM.

RILEY CALLED THROUGH — GRICE SQUEALED ON HIS WAY TO THE TITAN SHUFFLE.

THE FOURTH TRAITOR IS WINDSOR, AND THEIR CONTACT IN CONTROL IS YOUR OLD PAL DEGAULLE. GOT 'EM ON HOLD DOWNSTAIRS.

ON MY WAY.

CONTROL — DREDD. MAJOR'S COMMITTED SUICIDE. BETTER GET A CLEAN-UP CREW DOWN HERE.

THAT'S A ROJ, DREDD.

YOU'RE WASHED UP, DEGAULLE. YOUR CO-CONSPIRATORS ARE ALL DEAD OR ON THE TITAN TRIP — YOU'RE NEXT.

WANT TO TELL ME ABOUT ANYONE ELSE INVOLVED IN THE PLOT AGAINST ME, OR DO WE USE THE PENTATHOL?

DAMN YOU, DREDD! YOU'RE ENJOYING THIS!

I'M IN NO MOOD FOR YOUR BULL, DEGAULLE! WHO ELSE?

N-N-NO-ONE!

THERE'S NO-ONE, DREDD. WE COULDN'T TRUST THEM — THEY'RE ALL READY TO HAND THIS CITY TO THE DEMOCRATS IN THE REFERENDUM, JUST LIKE YOU.

THE FOOLS!

LIE DETECTOR CONFIRMS, DREDD. SHE'S THE LAST.

OKAY, CLOSE IT UP. TITAN SHUTTLE GOES IN FIVE.

I DON'T GET IT, DEGAULLE. WE MAY HAVE HAD OUR DIFFERENCES, BUT I ALWAYS THOUGHT YOU WERE A DAMN GOOD JUDGE. WHY THROW IT DOWN THE TOILET?

WHY—? HA!

BECAUSE I'M NOT A GRUDDAM ROBOT, DREDD!

FIFTEEN YEARS I'M ON THE STREETS — THEN SOME LITTLE PUNK TAKES HALF MY GUTS OUT WITH A LAS-BLASTER AND I WIND UP STUCK BEHIND A SCREEN IN CONTROL!

AND I JUST CAN'T STOP THINKING, JEEZ GRUD ABOVE — IS THIS ALL I GET OUT OF IT?

'IS THIS ALL I GET OUT OF IT...'

THAT WASN'T THE POINT. IT HADN'T CROSSED HIS MIND ONCE, NOT IN HIS TIME OF DOUBT, NOR WHEN THE CURSED EARTH STRETCHED BEFORE HIM, OLD SILVER'S "FAREWELL, DREDD" ECHOING IN HIS EARS — NOR WHEN HE WALKED AS A DEAD MAN, COMING BACK TO SAVE HIS CITY FROM NECROPOLIS.

CONTROL, WE'RE FINISHED HERE. INFORM THE CHIEF JUDGE I'M ON MY WAY.

WILCO.

NO, HIS PROBLEM HAD BEEN DIFFERENT.

HE'D TAKEN THE HIKE BECAUSE OF IT.

A YOUNG JUVE ASKED HIM QUESTIONS HE COULD FIND NO ANSWERS FOR, AND WHEN THE KID DIED DREDD FELT RESPONSIBLE FOR ALL OF IT.

INTERROGATION CUBES

RESPONSIBLE FOR A CITY WHERE FREEDOM WAS BOUND IN CHAINS OF IRON, AND JUSTICE WAS BUT A TINY FLICKER IN THE COLD, HARD LIGHT OF THE LAW.

WHERE THE JUDGES STAMPED ON PEOPLE WHO ASKED — PEACEFULLY — FOR NOTHING MORE THAN THE RIGHT TO DETERMINE THEIR OWN DESTINY.

AND YES, HE WAS RESPONSIBLE, JUST AS MUCH AS ANYONE WHO WORE THE EAGLE OF JUSTICE IN MEGA-CITY ONE.

BUT TO FEEL GUILT...TO FEEL GUILT WAS TO THINK LIKE A MAN, NOT A JUDGE.

BECAUSE WHERE A MAN WOULD BE WEAK, A JUDGE WOULD BE STRONG. WHERE A MAN WOULD FOOL HIMSELF THAT MILLIONS OF PEOPLE COULD LIVE TOGETHER IN PEACE, A JUDGE WOULD KNOW THAT THAT WAS JUST A PIPEDREAM, AND THAT IRON-FISTED LAW WAS NEEDED TO STOP MURDEROUS CHAOS.

AND MORE THAN ANYTHING ELSE, DREDD WAS A JUDGE.

HE DIDN'T **NEED** ANYTHING OUT OF IT. THE JOB WAS ITS OWN REWARD.

155 TOP FLOOR

THIRTEEN YEARS AGO HE'D BEEN RETURNING FROM HIS TOUR AS JUDGE MARSHAL OF LUNA-ONE, AND AS THEY WERE COMING IN ON THE SPACEPORT HE'D GLANCED OUT OF THE WINDOW.

FROM THAT HIGH UP THE CITY LOOKED BEAUTIFUL, LIKE A HUGE JEWEL ON THE EAST COAST – SUN DANCING ON THE GLASSEEN TOWERS, THE MEGA-WAYS CRISS-CROSSING IN A BLUR OF MOVEMENT, AND A MUTED NEON GLOW WINKING FROM THE CONSTANT TWILIGHT OF THE LOWEST LEVELS.

HOWDY, JOE. GLAD YOU COULD JOIN US.

HALF AN HOUR TO GO.

YEAH.

HE COULDN'T SEE THE **CANCER** FROM THAT DISTANCE, THE BLOATED EVIL **ROT** THAT TOUCHED EVERYONE BELOW AND CUT A FLAW IN THE JEWEL LIKE A GANGRENOUS WOUND.

BUT DREDD LOOKED OUT OVER THE CITY – **HIS** CITY – AND HE **KNEW**.

"MEGA-CITY ONE...EIGHT HUNDRED MILLION PEOPLE AND EVERYONE OF THEM A POTENTIAL **CRIMINAL**. THE MOST VIOLENT, EVIL CITY ON EARTH...BUT, GOD HELP ME, **I LOVE IT**."

ONE MINUTE 'TIL THE VOTE. LOOKS LIKE MOST FOLKS'VE MADE UP THEIR MINDS ALREADY, JOE.

KLIK!

APPEARANCES CAN BE DECEPTIVE, CHIEF JUDGE.

YEAH. SURE HOPE SO, ANYHOW.

HELL OF A RISK WE'RE TAKING HERE...

BUT A **VITAL** ONE.

THE DEMOCRATS HAVE GOT THE CITIZENS ON A KNIFE EDGE, HERSHEY. IT'S NOT ENOUGH TO JUST LAY IN WITH THE DAYSTICKS ANY MORE — THAT'S JUST STORING UP MORE TROUBLE.

NO, IF WE WANT TO CARRY ON WITH THE HEAVY DISCIPLINE THEN WE — AND THEY — HAVE TO KNOW THEY **WANT IT.**

THAT'S TRUE, JOE.

AND ANY SECOND NOW WE'RE GONNA **KNOW** ALRIGHT.

ALL OF US.

JUDGES OUT

PERHAPS EVEN THE **CITY** HOLDS ITS BREATH AS ITS CHILDREN VOTE ON THEIR FUTURE.

A HUSH LIES OVER THE CONCRETE JUNGLE, A SILENCE SO KISSED WITH DESTINY THAT IT **SCREAMS** THROUGH THE PEDWAYS AND ZOOM TUBES, AROUND THE BLOCKS AND MEZZANINES TO ECHO ACROSS THIS VAST METROPOLIS ON THIS HISTORIC DAY.

*C*AN YOU HEAR IT...?

DREDD CAN.

NOON. **THE CITIZENS VOTE.**

THUS THE CITIZENS WILL HAVE TO WAIT QUITE A BIT LONGER THAN IF THE VOTES WERE BEING TABULATED BY CURRENT MEGA-CITY TECHNOLOGY... ABOUT SIX MINUTES.

THE VOTES UPLOAD DIRECTLY INTO THE BALLOTEER MAINFRAME COMPUTER, BUILT IN 2067 FOR THE LAST PRESIDENTIAL ELECTION AND DUSTED OFF ESPECIALLY FOR THE FIRST REFERENDUM IN 46 YEARS.

THE CHOICE IS CLEAR —

JUDICIAL CONTROL...

OR DEMOCRACY.

THE IRON FIST OF THE LAW AND THE CERTAINTY OF RETRIBUTION. HARSH LAWS THAT MANY COULDN'T EVEN UNDERSTAND. THE GUN AND THE DAYSTICK.

OR —

RULE BY AN ELECTED GOVERNMENT, WITH LAWMAKERS AND LAWKEEPERS SEPARATE, EACH BALANCING THE OTHER'S POWER.

SOMETHING MOST CITIZENS HAVE NEVER KNOWN.

ARE YOU ALRIGHT, BLONDEL? DREDD'S A FASCIST **SCUMBAG**! HE TURNED THE MARCH INTO A SLAUGHTER, REMEMBER? HE THREW YOU IN THE **CUBES**!

HE GOT ME **OUT**, TOO.

THIS ISN'T JUST **ANYONE** WE'RE TALKING ABOUT, JON. IT'S **JUDGE DREDD**. YOU SAW THE VID REPORTS AFTER NECROPOLIS...

THE SISTERS OF DEATH BURNT HIS **FACE** OFF, AND HE JUST GOT RIGHT UP AND CAME BACK AND SAVED THE CITY! CAN YOU IMAGINE THE SHEER **GUTS** THAT MUST HAVE TAKEN?

I JUST WONDER SOMETIMES... WHY ARE WE FIGHTING A MAN LIKE THAT?

JEEZ, BLONDEL, YOU'RE NOT THINKING STRAIGHT. IT'S ALL THE STRESS OF THE VOTE... SO HE'S A TOUGH GUY. SO **WHAT**?

YOU SAID IT YOURSELF -- THE JUDGES'LL DO **ANYTHING** TO HANG ON TO THEIR PRECIOUS POWER! THEY **LOVE** IT!

WHY? THEY DON'T GET PAID, THEY DON'T HAVE LIVES OF THEIR OWN -- WHAT'S IN IT FOR **THEM**?

WHAT DO THEY **GET** OUT OF IT?

BLONDEL! JON! **THIS IS IT**!

RESULTS ARE IN, GUYS!

WELL, HERE WE GO, SWEETHEART...

IN A FEW SECONDS, THE JUDGES WON'T MATTER ANYWAY.

THIS IS THE MOMENT, PEOPLE. THE VOTES ARE IN AND ARE BEING DOWNLOADED DIRECTLY TO YOU NOW WITH NO HUMAN INTERVENTION.

GREETINGS, CITIZENS. I, THE RETURNING :clik: BALLOTEER MAINFRAME, CERTIFY THESE TO BE THE ACCURATE RESULTS OF THE :clik: REFERENDUM.

ONLY THIRTY-FIVE PERCENT OF CITIZENS EXERCISED THEIR GRUD-GIVEN RIGHT TO VOTE... THE POOREST TURN-OUT IN :clik: SEVENTY-FOUR YEARS.

IF YOU DON'T VOTE FOR FOR YOUR CANDIDATES, HOW DO YOU EXPECT THEM TO WIN?

GRUD! TWO HUNDRED CHANNELS AND THEY'RE ALL SHOWING THE SAME THING!

OF THE FORTY-THREE MILLION VOTES CAST, TWENTY-THREE PERCENT VOTED BOTH OPTIONS :clik: AND THUS FORFEITED THEIR VOTES.

"BETTER THE DEVIL YOU KNOW."

UH-HUH.

NINE PERCENT VOTED FOR THE :clik: DEMOCRATS...

AND SIXTY-EIGHT PERCENT FOR THE JUDGES.

THE JUDGES ARE DULY RETURNED FOR ANOTHER TERM OF OFFICE.

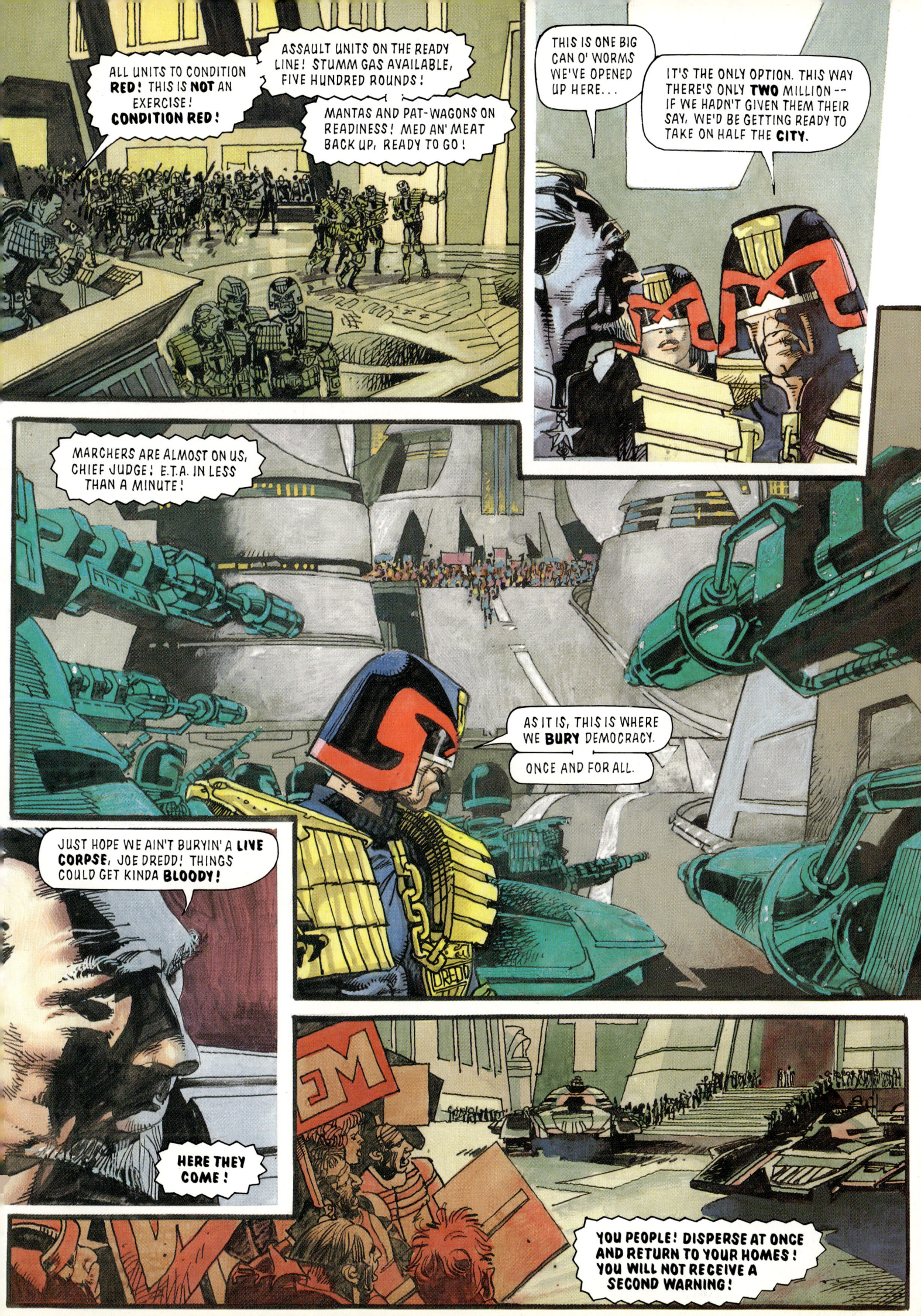

DUPRE.

DREDD.

TAKING A BIT OF A RISK COMING OUT HERE ALONE, AREN'T YOU? THERE'S TWO MILLION PEOPLE HERE.

THERE'S ENOUGH FIREPOWER BACK THERE TO WIPE OUT TEN TIMES THAT NUMBER -- BUT I DON'T NEED THAT TODAY.

YOU'RE GOING TO TURN ROUND AND GO HOME PEACEFULLY, EVERY LAST ONE OF YOU. AND I'LL TELL YOU WHY.

WE DIDN'T FIX ANYTHING, DUPRE. THE REFERENDUM WAS CARRIED OUT FAIR AND SQUARE AND THE PEOPLE VOTED FOR US BECAUSE THEY CAN RELY ON US -- BECAUSE THEY KNOW WHERE THEY STAND.

WE DIDN'T HAVE TO FIX IT.

DEMOCRACY'S NOT FOR THE PEOPLE -- NOT BECAUSE WE SAY SO, BUT BECAUSE THEY DON'T WANT IT.

YOU PEOPLE ARE DREAMERS. THAT'S OKAY IN ITS PLACE, BUT NOT WHEN YOU WANT TO RULE -- TO MAKE THE LAW IN THIS CITY.

BECAUSE HERE, I AM THE LAW.

BUT--

LET'S HEAR IT, DUPRE.

I...

YOU ARE THE LAW, JUDGE DREDD.

BLONDEL, ARE YOU **CRAZY**? WE –

OH FOR GRUD'S **SAKE**, JON! **LEAVE IT!**

BLONDEL DUPRE DIDN'T GO HOME THAT DAY. SHE WENT BACK TO THE DESERTED DEMOCRAT H.Q. AND SAT THERE UNTIL NIGHTFALL, THINKING ABOUT HER BROKEN HEART...

AND HER SHATTERED DREAMS.

BLONDEL?

JON...

YOU WEREN'T AT THE APARTMENT, HON. I WAS WORRIED.

I'M ALRIGHT. WHERE ARE ALL THE OTHERS?

THEY JUST WENT HOME, ALL OF THEM. I DON'T UNDERSTAND...

OH, JON, IT'S SIMPLE... DREDD'S **RIGHT**. WE'RE JUST USELESS DREAMERS. IT TAKES SOMEONE SPECIAL TO RULE **THIS** CITY. NOT US... WE'RE JUST LIKE EVERYONE ELSE, ALL THE PEOPLE WHO DIDN'T BOTHER TO VOTE, WHO DON'T WANT THE TROUBLE. WE JUST TOOK LONGER TO REALISE IT, THAT'S ALL. ALL WE CAN DO IS MAKE THE BEST OF WHAT WE'VE GOT.

WE'VE GOT EACH OTHER, SWEETHEART. I GUESS THAT'S ENOUGH FOR ME.

HERE OR ANYWHERE ELSE.

"I KNOW".

"MEGA-CITY ONE... EIGHT HUNDRED MILLION PEOPLE AND EVERYONE OF THEM A POTENTIAL CRIMINAL. THE MOST EVIL, VIOLENT CITY ON EARTH... BUT, GOD HELP ME, **I LOVE IT.**" *JUDGE DREDD, 2100.*

THE END

NEXT PROG: **BEAT THAT!**